the *Burston* School *Strike*

Burston School Strike!

A Village in Revolt!! **A Fight for Freedom and Justice!!!**

A MEETING

WILL BE HELD AT THE

Bermondsey Town Hall,

Spa Road, Bermondsey,

On TUESDAY, FEB. 22nd, 1916,

for a Rally and Call for Unity.

Chair to be taken at 8 p.m. by

Dr. ALFRED SALTER, J.P.,

WITH THE ASSISTANCE OF THE FOLLOWING SPEAKERS:

MR. AND MRS. HIGDON
(THE VICTIMISED SCHOOL TEACHERS) and Children from the School of Burston

CASEY AND HIS FIDDLE

MR. H. B. WALKER
(Gen. Sec. Agricultural Labourers' Rural Workers' Union)

MR. WILL GODFREY
(National Union of Vehicle Workers)

MR. W CARTER
(Organising Sec. N.U.R.)

MR. J. BIRMINGHAM
(Organising Sec. N.U.R.)

MR. JOHN SCURR
(" Herald ")

MR. W. J. CRAGIE
(Bermondsey Branch N.U R.)

Come and Hear for yourselves from Mr. and Mrs. Higdon and the brave women of Burston what they have suffered since April, 1914, and nobly struggled against the tyranny of Parson and Landowners!

LADIES ARE SPECIALLY INVITED!

Local Secretary: A. ROWLING,
182, Rolls Road, Bermondsey, S.E.

Prowde & Co., Printers (T.U.), 244, Old Kent Road.

OXFORD *Playscripts*

Series Editor – Bill Lucas

Roy Nevitt

the *Burston* School Strike

Oxford University Press

Oxford University Press, Great Clarendon Street, Oxford OX2 6DP

Oxford New York
Athens Auckland Bangkok Bogotá Buenos Aires
Calcutta Cape Town Chennai Dar es Salaam Delhi
Florence Hong Kong Istanbul Karachi Kuala Lumpur
Madrid Melbourne Mexico City Mumbai Nairobi Paris
São Paulo Singapore Taipei Tokyo Toronto Warsaw

and associated companies in
Berlin Ibadan

Oxford is a trade mark of Oxford University Press

The Burston School Strike
© Roy Nevitt 1992
Activities © Bill Lucas 1992
Published by Oxford University Press 1992
Reprinted 1992, 1997, 1998

All applications to perform this play should be addressed in the
first instance to the Permissions Controller, Educational Division,
Oxford University Press, at the address above.

A CIP catalogue record for this book is available from
the British Library

ISBN 0 19 831274 1

Typeset by Pentacor PLC
Printed and bound in the United Kingdom
at the University Press, Cambridge

Contents

An Introduction from the Editor

The Burston School Strike is probably not like other plays that you have read. This is because it is a special kind of play called a documentary.

You may have seen documentaries on television. They attempt to tell something as it really happened.

The problem with this is that it is impossible. Things cannot happen on stage exactly as they happened in real life many years earlier.

For a start, in **The Burston School Strike** you will notice that Roy Nevitt has divided what happened into two acts. He has also added songs. Although these were sung by people at the time this play is set, in the years leading up to the First World War, there is no guarantee that they sang them in the way they are used here.

In real life people sometimes give speeches which last a long time. They also use words which are difficult. In some plays, long speeches would be shortened and words made simpler. Because this is a documentary drama, the speeches here have deliberately been left as close as possible to how they originally were.

This means that there *are* some difficult speeches in the play which you may have to work at and which you may find more interesting when you have studied the Activities Section.

You may like to miss out the songs if you are reading the play in class or, better still, you may like to get together with musicians in your school or youth club and perform them.

You might just end up enjoying yourselves!

Bill Lucas

Characters
· · · · · · · · · · · ·

Supply teacher	*(non-speaking roles)*
Policeman	
Glebe Tenant	
Soldier	
Carter	*Official of the National Union of Railwaymen*
Roberts	*Official of the Agricultural and Rural Workers Union*
Sylvia Pankhurst	*Suffragette*

Supporters of the National Agricultural Labourers and Rural Workers Union. Tom Higdon is on the left.

Act 1
· · · · · ·

Scene 1

	The stage is initially in darkness. There are sounds of a train slowing down and stopping and then of doors slamming.
Porter	Diss! Diss! All out please! All out!
	The passengers leave; some are welcomed by friends. **Tom** *and* **Annie Higdon** *are left standing on the platform.*
Tom	Porter, porter!
Porter	Yes sir?
Tom	Why didn't we stop at Burston?
Porter	Cows back there on the line, sir, had to make up time.
Tom	How far is Burston?
Porter	About four miles.
Annie	Can anyone take us there?
Porter	No, ma'am. No one here till next train – three, four hours.
Tom	It looks as though we'll have to walk.
Annie	We walked out of Wood Dalling, Tom – we'll walk into Burston!
	Tom *and* **Annie** *go off.* *All the children including* **Marjorie, Violet** *and* **Rose** *enter, playing 'What's the time, Mr Wolf'. They stop and look as* **Annie** *and* **Tom** *come on.*
Tom	Is this Burston village?
Rose	Yes, sir.

Annie	Can you show us where the schoolhouse is?
Violet	Yes, ma'am, it's over there. Are you our new teachers?
Annie	Yes, we're Mr and Mrs Higdon. We shall see you in school tomorrow.

> *Tom* and *Annie* exit. The children watch them go.

Marjorie	I'll have to go now.
Rose	What did they say their name was?
Violet	Kingdom, wasn't it?
Marjorie	I think that's what they said.

> *The children run off.*

. . . .

Scene 2

> Enter **Mrs Wilby, Mrs Potter, Mrs Moore, Mrs Durbidge** and **Mrs Ling.**

Mrs Wilby	My lass met the new teachers last night.
Mrs Potter	They said their name was Kingdom.
Mrs Moore	The children said they were very nice.
Mrs Durbidge	We've had so many teachers here.
Mrs Ling	Let's hope these stay.

> *The women go off. The school bell rings and the children file into school.*

Annie	Good morning, children.
Children	Good morning Mrs Kingdom. Good morning Mr Kingdom.

Annie	No, children. Our name is Higdon. Mr and Mrs Higdon – H-i-g-d-o-n.

Annie writes this on the blackboard.

Tom	Sit down, children.

The children sit and put their hands on their heads.

Annie	Why are you sitting like that?
George	Our last teacher made us sit like that for the register.
Annie	You may take your hands down. May I have the register, Mr Higdon? Stand up as I call you, and say your Christian name.

Annie opens the register.

Annie	Bailey?
George	*(Standing)* George, ma'am.
Annie	Barnes?
Tommy	*(Standing)* Tommy, ma'am.
Annie	Bloomfield?
Henry	*(Standing)* Henry, ma'am.
Annie	Cotterill?

Silence.

Annie	Cotterill? Is Cotterill here?
Tommy	It's Albert.
Annie	Where is he? Is he ill?
Herbert	No ma'am, he's with Farmer – with Mr Gamble.

Tom	What is he doing there?
Herbert	Leading the horse, sir.

Henry starts to cry.

Tom	What's the matter, lad?
Emily	He wants to go to the toilet, sir.
Lily	Last teacher wouldn't let us go during lessons, sir.
Annie	Go along, Henry.

Henry goes off.

Annie   We shall start with a song. Stand up straight everyone. George, open the window – you must get fresh air into your lungs . . .

Eland enters bringing Henry by the ear.

Eland   Good morning Mrs Higdon, Mr Higdon. I am the Reverend Eland. Welcome to Burston. You are new in our parish and I myself have been appointed only a short time. I hope we can work together through the church and with the church's blessing. Why was this child not in class?

Annie   He had permission to leave, for good reason, Mr Eland.

Eland   I see. May I see the register please?

Annie hands it to him.

Eland   I'm pleased to see good attendance.

Tom   Albert Cotterill is absent, sir. He is not ill, but leading Farmer Gamble's horse. Is this condoned?

Eland   This is a farming community, Mr Higdon. The children are expected to help their elders at need. I shall not disturb you further, but expect to see you in church on Sunday. Good day.

Eland goes off.

Annie	Come, children, a deep breath – in – out – in – out. Let me see the air going in! Do you know 'Early One Morning'?
Children	Yes, ma'am.
Annie	I shall sing the first verse, then you join in . . .
	She starts to sing. After the first verse, she pauses.
Annie	Come along now . . .
	The children all join in. They leave the stage as the band picks up the tune.
Children	Early one morning Just as the sun was rising I heard a maiden singing In a valley below. Oh don't deceive me, Oh never leave me, How could you treat a poor maiden so?

. . . .

Scene 3

Several months have passed and it is spring. **Adam** *comes on, looks around and whistles.* **Elsie** *runs on looking flustered.*

Elsie	I've only got a minute. Mrs Eland will be wanting tea made . . .
Adam	I had to see you. Now that old Johnson's died, Farmer Gamble's found me a cottage.
Elsie	Oh . . .

Adam	Can't have a cottage for one. Elsie – will you marry me?
Mrs Eland	*(Off stage)* Elsie!
Elsie	I'll have to go . . .
Adam	Elsie! I want you to marry me!
Elsie	Oh Adam! I can't tell you now – not now – please!

> ***Elsie*** *runs off.*
> ***Mrs Eland*** *and* ***Elsie*** *can be heard talking offstage.*

Mrs Eland	Elsie – where have you been? Seeing that young man of yours and up to no good, I'll be bound.
Elsie	Oh no ma'am.
Mrs Eland	I pay you to work, my girl, not idle. Mr Eland's waiting for his tea – now get along.

> ***Adam*** *turns to see* ***Farmer Gamble.***

Gamble	Why aren't you at the plough, lad? What are you doing here?
Adam	Thought I saw a fox . . .
Gamble	Aye, one with two legs! Now get back to the plough. Young lad's been waiting there half an hour and more.

> ***Adam*** *goes off.* ***Gamble*** *turns as* ***Tommy*** *runs on.*

Tommy	Mr Gamble sir. Mr Higdon says Albert's to come to school, sir.
Gamble	Get back and tell Mr Higdon he'll be there when spring ploughing's done.

> ***Tommy*** *goes off. Moments later,* ***George*** *comes on with a folded piece of paper.*

George	Mr Gamble, I've got a message from our teacher for you . . .

Gamble takes the paper and tears it up.

Gamble   Get back to your teacher, lad. Tell him Albert's doing man's work, not idling in a schoolroom.

*George leaves the stage. Moments later, **Tom** strides onto the stage dragging **Albert** with him. Enter **Durbidge**, a poacher, who witnesses what follows.*

Tom   Gamble, you are deliberately keeping boys away from school – it's illegal, and I have asked you reasonably . . .

Gamble   Baaaaa!

Tom   . . . to allow them to attend school as their parents wish . . .

Gamble   Mooooo!

Tom   This is the third time you've taken Albert away from his lessons and have set him to work where he can be seen by the others . . .

Gamble   Woof! woof!

Tom   Gamble, this is intolerable – aren't you man enough to answer me?

Gamble   Get back in the schoolroom, Higdon. This is farm land – the land comes first and we need all hands to work it.

Tom   The children need education as well as learning love of the land. You school managers are undermining our efforts to teach them and to give them a warm dry schoolroom in which to learn . . .

Gamble   The lad'll learn more at the plough than anything you and your lady wife can teach him! High and mighty Lady Higdon!

Tom   You speak of my wife like that again and I'll stuff your head up the school chimney.

Gamble   I'll speak as I like, Higdon. It's time you learned your place here. Now get away, I've work to do . . .

Tom   And without Albert, Mr Gamble! Come with me, lad.

*Tom turns to leave the stage holding **Albert** by his arm. **Gamble** strikes at **Tom's** arm. **Tom** strikes **Gamble** who trips and stumbles. He swings at **Tom** who hits out and knocks **Gamble** to the ground.*

Durbidge   Plough him in, Tom! Plough him in!

*Tom exits with **Albert**.*

Gamble   *(From the ground)* I'll get you for that, Higdon! And one day I'll get you too, Durbidge, for your poaching!

Gamble gets up and goes off.

· ·

Scene 4

*It is summer. The women, including **Mrs Wilby**, **Mrs Potter**, **Mrs Moore**, **Mrs Durbidge** and **Mrs Ling**, come on from haymaking. One of them sings a folk song. Two children bring them cheese and bread. **Adam** brings on a jug of water which they pass around.*

Mrs Wilby   *(To Mrs Potter)* Why don't you go and sit down in the shade of the rick – you're flushed.

Mrs Potter   No, I'll be all right.

Mrs Moore   She shouldn't be here at all in her condition.

Mrs Durbidge   It makes no difference – she's got to.

Mrs Ling   We've all got to – how else would we live?

Annie enters with the children.

Annie   Now remember, when we get to the wood and the hedgerows, we pick just one flower of each kind. We shall take the summer back into the schoolroom, but we must also leave it for others to enjoy. *(To the women)* Good day. How beautiful it is in the sun.

Violet   Look, a poppy!

Marjorie   It's almost dead. There'll be fresh flowers in the shade – come along!

Rose   I'm going to find the first one!

Mrs Wilby   My schooling wasn't like that. But my lass is learning her arithmetic – she says Mrs Higdon makes it so clear.

Mrs Potter   The Higdons care about our children – you can tell that. Look what Mrs Higdon does for them when they're ill.

Mrs Moore   Mrs Higdon bought new boots for Tommy Barnes – and out of her own pocket.

Mrs Durbidge   Perhaps it'll be better for our children – they won't have to break their backs with long hours in the fields.

All exit.

· ·

Scene 5

*It is autumn and the time for Harvest Festival. The band plays 'Harvest Home', as the villagers, including **Elsie**, enter. **Adam** is not with them. They are followed by **Eland** and **Mrs Eland**. The children come on bringing harvest fruit, sheaves, etc. which they place at **Eland**'s feet. **Tom** and **Annie** enter at the end of the line of children.*

Eland   Welcome to church, Mrs Higdon. I had expected you to bring the children before this and join in Christian instruction.

Annie   Christianity goes beyond one church, Mr Eland. It is around us indoors and out, and we benefit daily from its influence.

The villagers sing two verses of 'Harvest Home'.

Villagers   Come, ye thankful people, come,
Raise the song of harvest-home!
All is safely gathered in,
Ere the winter storms begin;
God, our maker, doth provide
For our wants to be supplied;
Come to God's own temple, come,
Raise the song of harvest-home.

Then, thou church triumphant, come,
Raise the song of harvest-home!
All be safely gathered in,
Free from sorrow, free from sin,
There forever purified
In God's garner to abide;
Come, ten thousand Angels, come,
Raise the glorious harvest-home!

They exit as the band picks up the tune. **Mrs Wilby** *and* **Elsie** *are left on the stage.*

Elsie   *(To Mrs Wilby)* How do I look?

Mrs Wilby   You'll be the prettiest one there!

Elsie   I made the dress myself!

Mrs Wilby   Has Adam seen it?

Elsie   Not yet – it's a surprise.

Adam *enters looking very tired and dusty.* **Mrs Wilby** *goes off.*

Elsie   Adam – where have you been?

Adam   Covering the ricks – this weather won't hold till morning. Got to get back, Elsie – got to finish covering and stake them before night . . .

Elsie   Go back! But you've worked since dawn!

Adam   *(Half rueful, half laughing)* Won't get paid, else – and what would we live on then?

Elsie   But I've got a new dress – and I've been ready for ages!

Adam   Ready for what . . .?

Elsie   Harvest supper, Adam – I've been looking forward . . .

Adam   I can't, Elsie – I'm so tired and we're not through yet – I can't help it lass . . .

Adam *puts his arm around her.* **Elsie** *bursts into tears of disappointment. Both go off in different directions.*

. . . .

Scene 6

*It is winter. Enter **Mrs Wilby**, **Mrs Potter**, **Mrs Durbidge**, **Mrs Ling** and **Mrs Moore**. The band plays 'O Little Town of Bethlehem' as the children enter school. They sing one verse, then quietly hum the tune while the women speak.*

Children
O little town of Bethlehem
How still we see thee lie!
Above thy deep and dreamless sleep
The silent stars go by.
Yet in the dark streets shineth
The everlasting light;
The hopes and fears of all the years
Are met in thee tonight.

Mrs Wilby
It's been bitter cold these last few weeks – lot of whooping cough about.

Mrs Potter
Mrs Higdon says she'll close the school if the cold spell holds.

Mrs Durbidge
When the children got wringing wet in the rain, Governess lit a fire and dried their clothes – she does her best, but that schoolroom is a disgrace.

Mrs Ling   Our cottages are leaking and damp – no repairs done and no work for the men with the weather so bad.

Mrs Moore   And Christmas coming – won't be much to cheer us this year.

> *Women exit.*
> *The children sing the second verse of 'O Little Town of Bethlehem'. While they are singing* **Tom** *comes on with* **Adam.**

Children   Where children pure and happy
Pray to the blessed child,
Where misery cries out to thee,
Son of the mother mild;
Where charity stands watching,
And faith holds wide the door,
The dark night wakes, the glory breaks,
And Christmas comes once more.

Tom   How are you managing?

Adam   Not well. There's not enough work and you don't get even a living wage.

Tom   We must organize, Adam. Get together and let the union fight for you. They'll make sure that when the price of bread goes up, your wages will go up too, and they'll stand behind you when you demand proper housing and abolishment of the tied cottage! Listen Adam, you can't do it singly or alone – together and in strength you can get your rights.

Adam   The union wants dues, Tom!

Tom   Fourpence a week! That's not much for a new life and the chance to be a free man!

Adam   Where's it coming from, Tom? No – listen. I get fifteen shillings and sixpence a week. My wife gets twelve shillings for food, clothes, heat if we can afford it, light too. Rent is three shillings and a penny. That leaves fivepence for me – and if weather's bad or we're ill, that goes too. Where do I find fourpence for the union?

· ·

Scene 7

The parish council elections are approaching.
Tom *is already on stage.*
Noah Sandy *enters.*

Noah   Tom, I'd like to put your name forward for the parish council election. We need a strong voice, Tom. I've pressed for ten years for restoration of footpaths and bridges and for repairs and improvements to cottages – the roofs of some of our cottages are like sieves. In bad weather, water runs down the walls – the places are not fit for swine. I'm voted down every time, Tom – they don't even bother to listen. I'm just a smallholder against a majority of farmers and landlords. Look at the schoolroom – it's dark, damp and rotting. You and Governess have done more than anyone should with your own money – but it's not right, Tom. There's others would be with us, Tom . . .

Tom   Then why are there no working men on the parish council? Where are the labourers' union branches in the district? Farmworkers, all workers, are the rock-bottom foundation upon which a nation's life is reared – the actual producers of food – agricultural labourers – yet they are the worst paid and the worst treated workers in Norfolk. Get them represented on the parish council, Noah. I'll stand for election, but we have to elect more than you and me. We've got to get the labourers, Noah – come along. Let's get to work now.

*Tom and **Noah** exit. **Rose** and **Mabel** enter, carrying chairs.*

Rose   How many chairs do we need?

Mabel   Just seven, around a table.

Rose   That's the parish council members. What about the others?

Mabel   What others? No one else comes. No one else bothers. The old council is always the new council. No one else would dare come.

Rose   But Farmer Lord's gone. That's a space.

Mabel   Another farmer will fill his place.

Rose   But why don't our men get on the parish council to speak for us? Why must we do as we're told without our voice being heard?

Mabel	Because that's the way it's always been. But they say things are changing – there have been meetings – we'll see. There – all ready for the meeting.

Noah enters.

Noah	More chairs – quickly. The whole village is coming . . .

> *The villagers, including **Mr Wilby, Mrs Wilby, Mr Potter, Mr Moore** and **Mr Ling** enter. The atmosphere is electric and confident. **Gamble, Eland, Millard, Smith** and others of the old council enter from the other side. The mood grows tense. Men from both sides sit down, but many stand. Gamble's faction urge him to speak.*

Millard	Let's get started, Gamble.
Smith	Go on, man, open the meeting.
Gamble	We are here to elect the parish council for the coming year.

> *There is a rustle of anticipation among the villagers. Some murmurs are heard.*

Gamble	There has been some mild disagreement in our village – and certain people who do not understand our ways have tried to use this to create discord. I have reason to believe that the votes as counted do not reflect the wishes and welfare of this parish.
Mr Wilby	Let's hear the count!
Mr Potter	You counted the votes – let's have it!
Mr Moore	What are we waiting for?
Noah	Mr Gamble, gentlemen – the vote for the parish council was canvassed fairly, the people of our parish cast their votes, and they have been counted. Let us hear the results.
Gamble	I do not wish to, nor will I, make an announcement which makes a mockery of the council!

| **Mr Ling** | Let a better man do it! |
| | |

Mr Wilby   Noah, read the count.

Noah   Mr Gamble, it is the will of those assembled, the people of our parish, that we should hear the names of those we have chosen to represent us!

Gamble is urged by his colleagues to give in.

Eland   Come on Gamble, read the count.

Millard   There is nothing to be gained by refusing.

Gamble   I will not be part of this abomination. The whole business is a mockery.

He slams the paper down in front of **Noah.**

Gamble   You do it!

Gamble storms out followed by one or two members of his party.

Noah   Thank you. The vote was cast as follows:

Mr Gamble (farmer) ten votes
Mr Millard (landlord) eleven votes
Mr Cobb (farmer) seventeen votes – elected
Mr Smith (landlord) ten votes
Mr Eland (rector) nine votes

Mrs Wilby   And one of them his own!

Mr Wilby   Shh, shh.

Noah   Mr Potter (labourer) twenty-five votes – elected
Mr Sandy (smallholder) twenty-eight votes – elected
Mr Higdon (schoolmaster) thirty-one votes – elected
Mr Jackson . . .

Noah's voice is drowned by the uproar and cheering.

Noah   Quiet please, quiet. In the absence of an elected chairman and until a full meeting can be held – I put it to this assembly that Mr Tom Higdon, with thirty-one votes, be asked to take the chair.

Mr Wilby   Carried.

Mr Potter   Take the chair, Tom.

Mr Moore   Speech, speech.

Tom *goes to the table and shakes* **Noah** *by the hand.*

Tom   Brothers, friends. By an overwhelming vote you have shown your confidence in the men who share your working lot. Let those men, let us, now show that we are worthy of your trust. Let those who work with their hands show their worthiness to receive a rightful share of the fruits of their labours. We are pledged to make our parish a good place for our wives and families. Your rents will go to the long delayed repair and restoration of your homes and your countryside, and to warm dry schools for your children.

There are cheers from the crowd.

You have fought the old order and won. We can build a Burston to be proud of, for ourselves and for the future. Thank you all.

The villagers start singing the 'Union Song',
quietly at first then more strongly as they leave
the stage. The brass band continues.

Villagers   Come all you bold fellows that follow the plough
Either hedging or ditching or milking the cow
The time has arrived and the Union flag waves
We won't be kept down like a lot of white slaves,
We won't be kept down like a lot of white slaves.

From Burston and Shimpling we'll meet on the green
For the fat bellied farmers we don't care a bean
From Diss and Winfarthing and Tivetshall too
We'll come with flags flying and ribbons of blue.

You may now tell the farmers you'll be slaves no more
The starvation wages you will not endure
Though you worked night and day you could not satisfy
They treated you worse than a pig in a sty.

The farmers will very soon find I am sure
That a man is a man be he never so poor
And no better man can in England be found
Than the hardworking man who is tilling the ground.

All England will learn of our doings today
As in grand procession we all march away
And the downtrodden labourers will cry as they go
With God and Tom Higdon we'll vanquish our foe.

George Edwards with the union banner.

Scene 8

Tom and Annie are in the schoolroom. The children are sitting at their desks.

Annie *(Whispering)* Tom, look at this letter from Mrs Philpot. She's complaining about a boy being rude to the two Barnardo girls she fosters.

Tom *(Whispering)* What is the boy supposed to have done?

Annie *(Whispering)* Something indecent. *(Speaking out loud)* Gladys Cleaver – come out here, please.

Gladys comes out.

Which boy did those rude things that you complained of to your foster mother?

Gladys *(Pointing)* It was him; that boy.

Annie Billy? Really? Well, we'll look into the matter later. Now go and sit down.

Tom is studying the register.

Annie *(To the class)* Before we separate for our arithmetic and our French lessons, I must tell you what we have planned for our young visitors from London. You must help them to enjoy their holiday in the country – most of them have never been out of the city before.

Rose They're so funny, Mrs Higdon! One of them asked me what was that animal with sticks on its head! Fancy – it was Mrs Philpot's cow!

Annie It is very unkind to laugh, Rose. You would say some foolish things, I'm sure, if you went to a big city, and it would hurt you to be laughed at. You must be patient and help them, all of you.

All Yes, Mrs Higdon.

Annie Tomorrow we shall invite them here for tea. In the morning we'll bake and make the school look as nice as we can.

All Oh yes, Mrs Higdon!

Tom	Annie, look at the register. *(Passes it to Annie)* Billy was not present at school on the day when the rude conduct that Gladys accuses him of was supposed to have taken place.
Annie	Gladys, come out here please, dear. You had not been in this school above one day before you were making accusations about one of the boys for being rude. Now why did you do that?
Gladys	He was. He did those rude things in the playground.
Annie	Which boy was it? Be very careful. Point him out again.

***Gladys** points to **Billy** again.*

Annie	Now, Gladys, it is very wicked to tell false stories. Billy was absent from school on that day. He couldn't have done what you say he did. Were you telling lies? (***Annie** speaks to the second girl*) Ethel Cummings, come out. Now that this little girl has come to stay with you at Mrs Philpot's, I hope you are not getting her into trouble and teaching her some of your bad ways.
Ethel	It wasn't nothing to do with me, ma'am.
Annie	But you have done things like this before and got into trouble for it, haven't you?
Ethel	Yes ma'am. But it was her – I didn't tell her to say those things.
Annie	Gladys, why did you say those things, knowing them to be false?
Gladys	It isn't false, ma'am. A boy did those things.
Annie	But which boy? It wasn't Billy, was it?
Gladys	It was another boy.
Annie	Which one? Point him out to me. But make sure you are telling the truth.
Gladys	He's not here.
Annie	Where is he then? All the boys are present today.

Gladys	It was a boy in my last school.
Annie	Then why did you tell such wicked lies?
Gladys	Mrs Philpot told us to.
Annie	Your foster mother told you to tell lies? Is this true, or are you still pretending?
Ethel	She said she'd beat us if we didn't.
Annie	Has she ever hit you?

Ethel and *Gladys* do not answer.

Emily	Please, ma'am, Mrs Philpot is always hitting her foster children. Everyone in the village knows it.

Eland enters.

Tom	Good morning, Reverend.
Eland	Good morning, sir. Mrs Higdon, why were you absent from school yesterday afternoon?
Tom	Look here Eland . . .
Annie	Now Tom – Mr Eland, I went to the station to meet the children from London and saw them safely disposed in their lodgings. We shall entertain them here in the school tomorrow – and I am ashamed! No warmth, peeling paint, rotting roof – no better than the slums they come from! The managers should be ashamed to permit our children to be educated in a hovel. You claim to provide heat – we have been expected to teach in a temperature of thirty-one degrees!
Eland	This is not the place or time for your complaints, Mrs Higdon. Bring them before the managers at the proper time.
Tom	We *have* complained – we have provided details and made proper requests. Nothing has been done.
Eland	You have overstepped all bounds in your unfounded demands and your rude insistence. I shall inform the managers of your attitude.

Eland storms off.
The children stare after him. **Annie** *picks up a*
poetry book and opens it.

Annie   Now children, we will leave arithmetic and French for today.
Instead, who can remember the poem we studied last week? The
one about a man who loved his fellow men.

Rose   Please Mrs Higdon, it was called 'Abou Ben Adhem' by James
Leigh Hunt.

Annie   Thank you, Rose. Very good. Please read it to us.

She hands **Rose** *the open poetry book and*
Rose *reads the poem out loud.*

Abou Ben Adhem (may his tribe increase)
Awoke one night from a deep dream of peace
And saw – within the moonlight in his room
Making it rich and like a lily in bloom –
An angel, writing in a book of gold.
Exceeding peace had made Ben Adhem bold
And to the presence in the room he said,
'What writest thou?' – the vision raised its head
And with a look made of all sweet accord
Answered, 'The names of those who love the Lord.'
'And is mine one?' said Abou. 'Nay, not so,'
Replied the angel. Abou spoke more low,
But cheerily still, and said, 'I pray thee then
Write me as one that loves his fellow men.'
The angel wrote and vanished. The next night
It came again with a great wakening light
And showed the names whom love of God had blessed
And lo! Ben Adhem's name led all the rest.

Tom, **Annie** *and the children freeze.*
Enter **Mrs Wilby, Mrs Potter, Mrs Moore,**
Mrs Durbidge *and* **Mrs Ling**. *They carry*
copies of the local newspaper.

Mrs Wilby   *(Reading)* The Burston Rebellion!

Mrs Potter	*(Reading)* Tom Higdon leads the parish council!
Mrs Moore	*(Reading)* Labourers take over Burston council!
Mrs Durbidge	*(Reading)* Village rector loses election!
Mrs Ling	There's a photograph of our husbands on the front page!
Mrs Wilby	Eland will be furious when he sees this.

They all exit.

· ·

Scene 9

*Enter **Eland, Gamble** and **Smith**.*

Smith   She wrote it in the school logbook – how the registers were not marked in the afternoon on account of the Harriers meeting – it being the custom of the schoolboys to follow the hounds. She writes how she took the girls for sewing in the afternoon and – just listen to this – *(Reads from a note)* 'Invited those boys who cared for better work than hunting an innocent hare to death, to return to school'. Better work than hunting an innocent hare to death. Sure enough, several boys did return to school and took reading, while the girls sewed, after which a 'story' was told by the Mistress. It's all in the logbook. I say this Higdon pair are turning Burston upside down, and setting the people against those who know what's best for them. They're a pair of rotten apples; we've got to throw them out before the rot spreads further.

Gamble   Higdon's mad. He's dangerous. We've always used the boys on the farms, but this trouble-maker thinks he's got the right to change our ways. He's a school teacher – he should keep his meddling fingers off the farms. Try to put him in his place and what do you get? Black eye, cut face and a bruised back's what I got! He should have been locked up but what did they do at the Sessions? A fine of forty shillings and twelve shillings and sixpence costs! He'll pay more than that before I've finished.

Smith   He's stirring up the men with all this union talk. They're never behind the plough where they ought to be – and I'm paying for it! No – they're off to some meeting without a by-your-leave!

Millard enters. He is furious.

Millard	Look at this! *(Throws a newspaper on the table)* 'The Burston Rebellion!' – and a photograph. The Higdons are running the paper as well as the village.
Gamble	It's an outrage! We should sack them here and now – we've got the right, haven't we?
Eland	Not quite, Mr Gamble. The Higdons are responsible to us as the school managers, but they're employed by the Norfolk Education Committee.
Smith	Then we write to Norwich and they'll sack them.
Eland	On what grounds?
Smith	What grounds! Do I have to tell you? You well know the arrogance of that woman and you've had the sharp edge of her tongue. She rides roughshod over all of us . . .
Eland	That in itself – unpalatable as it is to all of us – is not ground enough for the Education Committee to dismiss the Higdons.
Gamble	Why not?
Eland	Because the Committee would require certain proof – which we do not at the moment have. With only our recommendation the Committee would not act for fear of action by the Teachers' Union.
Gamble	The blasted unions again! They're dragging the country into the gutter – it'll end in bloodshed and revolution, you can be sure!
Millard	Eland's right. We've got to back up our feelings with facts.
Smith	Then I'll give you facts! That woman spends school money on coal without permission – and wastes it by lighting fires without reason or need.
Eland	That's better. Then there are the unending complaints.
Millard	Complaints alone are not enough, and several – such as the drains and the pump – received attention.

Eland begins the letter, writing as he speaks.

Eland   'Since the appointment of Mrs Higdon to Burston School, the managers have offered her every assistance and have co-operated to the full with her requests for alterations and additions to the building, including installation of a new heating system.'

Gamble takes over the dictation of the letter and Eland continues to write it down.

Gamble   'Our efforts have been met with resentment, discourtesy and blatant disregard of our instructions that open fires were unnecessary and to be discontinued.'

Smith   Then what about the time she closed the school for a week just after Christmas?

Eland   *(Surprised)* What was that?

Smith   You didn't know? That's right, you were in Switzerland.

Gamble   She took it on herself to close the school because of whooping cough.

Eland   There's always been whooping cough in Burston every winter – but the school was never closed.

Millard   It was more serious and widespread than usual.

Eland   Was an epidemic declared by a medical man?

Millard   Not to my knowledge.

Eland   So Mrs Higdon includes the practice of medicine among her many talents! You say she closed the school on her own initiative?

Smith   Indeed she did – just as she'd close your church if she had a chance!

Gamble   I'm wondering – can we raise that charge made by the Barnardo children who stayed with Mrs Philpot?

Eland   That's right. Let's add it to our letter to the Education Committee.

Eland continues the letter, writing as he speaks.

Eland	'In December Mrs Philpot, foster mother of two little girls from Dr Barnardo's Homes, had occasion to write to Mrs Higdon concerning the indecent conduct of some boys in the school playground, which these girls were compelled to witness.'
Gamble	'Mrs Higdon accused those girls of lying and giving false witness . . .'
Smith	'. . . subjected them to cross questioning before the whole school . . .'
Millard	'. . . punished them by keeping them in during playtime, day after day . . .'
Smith	'. . . and by whipping.'
Eland	'The managers find these charges against the girls utterly without foundation and the continued reference to this unpleasant subject detrimental to the school's tone and discipline. Owing to the insubordination . . .'
Gamble	'. . . and rudeness . . .'
Eland	'. . . of the Mistress, the managers find it impossible to work with her . . .'
All	'. . . and respectfully request that she be transferred.'

*Enter **Elsie**.*

Eland	Ah, Elsie . . .
Elsie	Please sir, tea's ready.
Eland	Shall we go . . .?

*The men exit, followed by **Elsie**.*

. . . .

Scene 10

Tom and Annie are in the schoolroom. Enter Ikin, an official from the Norfolk Education Committee.

Ikin   What is wrong between you and the Managers. Mrs Higdon?

Annie   I am not aware of anything wrong.

Ikin   The Norfolk Education Committee have received written complaints, Mrs Higdon. You have been obstructive, discourteous and unnecessarily harsh in the disciplining of children . . .

Annie   What? Harsh with my discipline?

Tom   They're dragging up the Barnardo issue again, Annie. Mr Ikin, if either the Reverend Eland, who has now made his wife a school manager and himself chairman of the school managers, or the Rector of Shrimpling had come to the school at our request, they would have heard the girls themselves deny that they were caned in school.

Annie   Neither will come, because they don't want the truth to come out.

Tom   Annie, you must consult the N.U.T. and get them to force the Education Committee to hold an inquiry.

Annie   I will, Tom, but be ready for trouble. We now have two parsons and a parson's wife plus a farmer and two landlords as our school managers. And the sub-committee for the inquiry will consist of landlords and farmers, too. In the eyes of such gentlemen, your agitation for labourers' unions will be a crime. They'll make up their minds to dismiss us.

Tom   They'll get at you, through me, like they did at Wood Dalling.

Ikin   You will get your inquiry, Mrs Higdon – and you will be required to answer the charges brought forward by the managers. Good day.

. . . .

Scene 11

*Half the stage shows scenes from the inquiry.
In the other half, **Annie** is reporting the whole
event to **Tom**, who was not allowed to attend
the inquiry. On stage throughout the scene are
the **President of the Education Committee**
on one side, and **Tom** and **Annie** on the other.
Enter **Eland**.*

Eland	*(Speaking to the **President**)* She is a dangerous woman. Not a proper person for young girls to associate with.

__Eland__ freezes.

Annie	Eland was there. He brought in a lawyer from Norwich.
Tom	He needed a lawyer to bolster up his rotten case.
Annie	An old woman said she saw some boys misbehaving . . .

*__Tom__ and __Annie__ freeze.
Enter __Old woman__.*

Old woman	*(Speaking to the **President**)* I saw some infant boys in the playground doing some very rude conduct, yes sir.

__Old woman__ freezes.

Tom	That old woman's own behaviour is scandalous in this parish. Rude conduct indeed. What about her own?

*__Tom__ freezes.
Enter __Gladys Cleaver__.*

President	Why did the Mistress cane you?

__Gladys__ remains silent.

President	Was it for saying the boy was rude to you?
Gladys	Yes sir.

*The **President** and **Gladys** freeze.*

Annie   He put words into the child's mouth, Tom.

Tom   Where was our King's Counsel? Was he struck dumb? Letting false statements go unchallenged?

***Tom** and **Annie** freeze.*
*Enter **Mrs Philpot**.*

Annie   Mrs Philpot was there.

Tom   She's the one most likely to have put those scars on the Barnardo girls' backs.

***Tom** and **Annie** freeze.*

Mrs Philpot   I'm not dead yet. I'm not dead yet.

***Mrs Philpot** freezes.*

Annie   It was a farce, Tom. The K.C. didn't cross-examine the Barnardo children at all. He did not even try to put up a fight.

Tom   Did you remind him that we had a witness who'd been waiting all afternoon to testify against Mrs Philpot?

Annie   He told me he was keeping her back for a slander action against Eland.

***Tom** and **Annie** freeze.*

President   The sub-committee finds that the head teacher has been discourteous to the managers.

*The **President** freezes.*

Tom   Discourteous to the managers – yes. She failed to bow to Miss Eland, the Rector's daughter, as she whizzed past on a bicycle one day during the Christmas holidays. Oh yes, and she supposedly gave Mrs Eland a cold reception one afternoon when she visited the school – and yes – one day, when Eland passed her in the road, during the Barnardo business, and said 'Good day', she failed to reply. That's the extent of her discourtesy.

Tom freezes.

President   In view of the direct conflict of evidence with respect to the caning of the Barnardo children, we are not able to give a decision on this matter.

*The **President** freezes.*

Tom   Well, the caning charge collapsed. That was something. What could they make of the rest?

Tom freezes.

Eland   (*To the **President***) The Higdons have been writing letters to Dr Barnardo's Homes asking that body to investigate the conditions in which their children are fostered in Burston. I have the letters here. They were forwarded to me as the organization's local secretary.

Eland freezes.

Tom   Eland quoted from my letters. I wrote those letters, not you. They told me to stay away from the inquiry, that I was not involved. Yet my letters were used. They were inadmissible evidence. Why didn't the K.C. object?

Tom freezes.

Eland   (*To the **President***) Here Mr Higdon's letter refers to this girl as 'somewhat mentally and morally deficient'. It contains other language difficult to justify.

Eland freezes.

Tom   I could justify it all right. The Barnardo children's foster father committed an unspeakable offence in his youth. In these letters I asked the Barnardo Homes to consider whether a man, guilty of such a crime, could ever be fit to have charge of the well-being of the Barnardo children.

Tom freezes.

President   We are strongly of the opinion that there is no evidence at all that the girl is mentally and morally deficient, or a danger to the school, as stated in the letters. In the opinion of the sub-committee, these children are well-treated and cared for by their foster mother, and these children are not afraid of being beaten by her.

Mrs Philpot   Victory! Victory! Victory!

President   The sub-committee, after most carefully reviewing the whole of the evidence, advise: that it is to the interest of elementary education in this village that the head teacher should seek other employment with as little delay as possible.

*The **President** and **Mrs Philpot** freeze.*

Annie   We're dismissed again, Tom, and on wicked, trumped-up charges.

Tom   It's Wood Dalling again, Annie – the same resentment because we fight for a better life for the men – for no more than their rights!

Annie   I won't accept this, Tom – not this time. I won't move from the schoolhouse.

. . . .

Scene 12

Violet, Marjorie, Rose and other children gather outside the schoolroom.

Rose   My mother says they're trying to get rid of our teachers.

Marjorie   How can they do that? No one wants them to go. What would we do if they went?

They file into the schoolroom.

Violet   We don't know they're going yet.

Annie is standing by her desk reading a letter. Tom is sorting through a pile of books.

Annie   Good morning, children.

Children   Good morning, Mrs Higdon. Good morning, Mr Higdon.

Annie   Violet, may I have the register please.

The children are tense and expectant.

Violet   (*Giving her the register*) Here ma'am – ma'am, Governess, please, is
                 it true they're sending you away?

Annie   Yes, Violet. Mr Higdon and I have been dismissed by the
                 Education Committee . . .

Marjorie   We don't want you to go.

Rose   You can't go away.

Annie   Children, children, quiet please! We are in the schoolroom. You
                 must be quiet while I finish the register) (*She glances around the room
                 and then writes in the register*) All here but Tommy and Christine.

                                              *The register is signed and returned to **Violet**.*

Annie   Now Marjorie, please hand out paper and drawing materials. Mr
                 Higdon and I have things to discuss but we shall not be very long.
                 Quiet and orderly all of you. You may choose the subject for your
                 drawing but I wish to see neat work.

                                              ***Annie** and **Tom** exit. The children sit still for
                                              a moment or two, then **Violet** gets up.*

Violet   We can't let them be taken away!

Henry   I don't want any other teachers!

Emily   What can we do?

Herbert   We mustn't let them go!

Lily   How can we keep them here?

Marjorie   Violet, what can we do?

Violet   We won't come to school tomorrow!

George   We could have a march!

Emily   What'd your mother say? She'd never let you stay away from school!

Lily   My mother would! She says Governess is the best teacher ever!

Violet   We'll all march! Hands up those who'll march!

The children shout and wave their hands in the air.

Marjorie   We'll march with banners!

Herbert   When, Violet, when?

This is picked up by others, until all the children are shouting 'When?'. **Violet** *holds her hands up for silence.*

Violet   Tomorrow morning – we'll meet on the village green and march past the school. We're not going to any school without Governess and Master!

George   Hooray, no school.

Emily   No school without our teachers.

Violet   Listen! Listen! Tomorrow morning at nine o'clock we all meet on the village green. Tonight we make banners. Tell your mothers. Make them help. We'll tell everybody!

Violet goes to blackboard. The whole class speaks the sentence word by word as she writes 'We are going on strike tomorrow'. She turns to class. There is a stunned silence – blackout. Band.

Act 2
· · · · · ·

Scene 1

*In blackout. A hubbub of voices grows as the villagers assemble on the village green. Lights up. **Tom** and **Annie** are among the crowd. They gather in groups talking excitedly. An atmosphere of expectation grows to a climax. Enter **Durbidge** and **Sutton**, a Methodist preacher. **Durbidge** is carrying a stool.*

Mr Wilby   Good old Durbidge.

Mr Potter   Got your gun, Durbidge?

Mr Moore   How many pheasants d'you get today, Durbidge?

Durbidge   Never mind that! I've got no pheasants in my bag tonight. I've got business: to consider the school question and the steps which should be taken. But don't look to me for speeches. John Sutton's the man for that. You tell 'em, John.

                   ***Durbidge** puts down the stool and **Sutton** steps up onto it.*

Sutton   Friends, the charges against the Higdons were lies. It was downright wicked to bring the Barnardo girls back to repeat their lies before a committee. Wicked to build up the charges of discourtesy to the managers and insubordination so that the Higdons could be dismissed. Join with me – let the managers know we protest against their vicious lying and injustice. Their motives have nothing to do with education! They're bitter because they're not getting it all their way any more. They're bitter about the union, Tom Higdon's success and their defeats. Why should they send away our teachers because they don't attend a certain church or live the way the managers think they should do!

Mrs Wilby   We're the parents and we're satisfied with our children's education.

Sutton   We know they're good teachers and we don't want them replaced with Parson's people and parish busybodies who have no regard for us, or our children, and no minds for anything but malice and lying rumour against those who stand for right and justice. *They* should be dismissed – not our teachers! We are satisfied with our school and with our teachers. Our children are well and happy. We want to keep our teachers and they want to stay. Let us fight to keep them! That's all I've got to say, friends. Fight!

Sutton steps down.

Durbidge   Before I put the resolution, does anyone want to speak?

Mr Wilby   It was the same when they were up at Wood Dalling. I've heard about it. Tom was doing union work there too. That's why the farmers didn't like him – that's why they got them out!

Mrs Potter   Mrs Higdon lit the fire when it was cold and the children's clothes were sopping wet! Would Vicar let his children sit in wet clothes all day long?

Mrs Moore   We won't stand for it! Why should we? They're our kids, aren't they? Don't we have a say?

Mr Ling   They're good teachers. My boy's getting on all right there. He likes school now.

Mrs Moore   It's a scandal, that's what it is! It's a lot of lies! Mrs Higdon never ill-treated those girls! Everyone here knows that, don't they? Everyone knows it! Eland knows it!

Roars of agreement.

Mr Ling   Eland's mad because Tom Higdon's chairman of the parish council and he couldn't even get on it! And because Tom Higdon's working with George Edwards for the union!

Mr Potter   Tom Higdon's father was a farmworker in Somerset, so he knows what he's talking about. This is just what happened up at Wood Dalling! The farmers on the managers' board didn't like his union work, so they got together and cooked up something to get rid of the both of them.

Durbidge   I'm going to propose a resolution, *(reads)* 'That we, the people and ratepayers of Burston, and the parents of the children attending Burston School, do most emphatically protest against the high handed action of the Education Committee in terminating the services of Mr and Mrs Higdon at the Burston School. Under the unjust circumstances, we protest against the introduction of new teachers into the school, and we urgently request the Education Committee to reconsider the whole matter with a view to our retention of the teachers whose services are so generally appreciated among us. That owing to the mischievous interference with the conduct of the school in regard to the Barnardo children, we protest against their attendance at the school and their presence in the parish.'

All roar approval.

'I further move that we refuse to send our children to the council school until justice is done to Mr and Mrs Higdon.'

Again everyone agrees.

We'll send our resolutions to the Education Committee, to our M.P., and to the President of the Board of Education in the Government! They can stick their plans!

Applause.
They all start to sing the last verse of the 'union song' and leave the stage in different directions.

All

All England will learn of our doings today
As in grand procession we all march away
And the downtrodden labourers will cry as they go
With God and Tom Higdon we'll vanquish our foe.

Tom and Annie remain on the stage.
Enter Ikin.

Tom

Good day, sir. Seven o'clock in the morning is unusual even for a formal visit – to what do we owe this attention?

Ikin

Mr Higdon – I have here your cheque and Mrs Higdon's in lieu of notice.

Tom

We are entitled to three months' notice, sir.

Ikin	It is the wish of the Education Committee that your employment terminate at once. Mrs Higdon, when will it be convenient for you to move out of this house?
Annie	It will not be convenient, Mr Ikin.
Ikin	The house will be required, Mrs Higdon. When will you move?
Annie	I don't know, Mr Ikin. I cannot say.

Annie turns and goes off.

Tom	Mr Ikin, a cheque in lieu of notice, presented without warning, does not permit the Education Committee to take possession of the schoolhouse before completion of the three months to which we are entitled.
Ikin	I am not going to argue, Mr Higdon. I am merely acquainting you with the decision of the Education Committee and asking on their behalf when Mrs Higdon will vacate the schoolhouse.
Tom	And Mrs Higdon has told you that she doesn't know!

Tom goes off.
*Enter **Eland, Supply Teacher, Policeman, Smith, Gamble, Mrs Eland** and **Millard**.*

Eland	Good day, Mr Ikin. The Education Committee has sent us this excellent lady to act as supply teacher now that the Higdons are going.
Millard	There was a meeting on the village green last night; the villagers were angry. I hope there'll be no trouble.
Eland	Gentlemen. Today is the first of April and the villagers are making fools of themselves. They'll forget the Higdons soon enough and Burston will come to its senses again. This whole wretched affair will be no more than a nine-day wonder.
Ikin	Then let us get the children into the schoolroom. It is time discipline was restored.

Ikin rings the bell.
The children assemble in response to the bell and approach the school. At the gate one child plays a few bars of 'The Red Flag' on a portable musical instrument. A sea of banners appears from nowhere, stating 'We want justice', 'We want our teachers back', etc. The children process round and round the officials, singing 'The Red Flag' accompanied by the band. The villagers enter and join in.

Children

The people's flag is deepest red,
It shrouded oft our martyred dead,
And ere their limbs grew stiff and cold,
Their hearts' blood stained its every fold.

So raise the scarlet standard high,
Beneath its shade we'll live or die,
Though cowards flinch and traitors sneer,
We'll keep the red flag flying here.

With heads uncovered swear we all,
To bear it onwards till we fall,
Come dungeons dark and gallows grim,
This song shall be our battle hymn.

So raise the scarlet standard high,
Beneath its shade we'll live or die,
Though cowards flinch and traitors sneer,
We'll keep the red flag flying here.

The officials leave the stage. The children and villagers cheer and wave their banners.

Scene 2

*It is Sunday and **Sutton** is addressing a crowd of villagers, including **Tom** and **Annie**, on the village green.*

Sutton   Friends and fellow Christians, here under God's Heaven on Burston Green, let us join in prayer. Lord God, we do try to carry on the work of thy Son, the friend of the poor, in this beautiful land, but it is not easy. Help us to be unafraid of the consequences when we do what we know we ought to do. Help us to meet injustice bravely, to be loyal and steadfast to our friends, to continue our struggle for the right with stout hearts. Help us to recognize good, true people and not let them down. Help us to do thy work on earth, guided by the example of thy Son, Jesus Christ. Amen.

Crowd   Amen.

Sutton   Everybody with a sense of justice is disgusted with the way the Parson has treated the Higdons. He got them out of the school by lies. But it's not just the church people who work from vengeance and spite. Farmer Fisher got the leader of the Primitive Methodist Church to condemn me for holding these services on the village green and in protest eight members of Burston Chapel resigned. Fisher is a chapelman and Parson is a churchman, and both are united in their opposition to Mr and Mrs Higdon. Both would stoop to anything to get them out. But we don't need the church or the chapel for worship. We can worship on Burston Green.

Annie   And as long as this beautiful weather lasts, we can do without a school to teach the children in. We'll teach them on Burston Green.

· ·

Scene 3

The same Sunday. On one half of the stage is **Eland**'s *pulpit. He is addressing his congregation of three:* **Mrs Eland, Gamble** *and* **Smith**. *The other half of the stage is to be occupied by other characters throughout the scene.*

Eland   St Paul's Epistle to the Ephesians, Chapter 6, verses 2 to 7.

'You who are children must show obedience in the Lord to your parents; it is your duty. Honour thy father and thy mother. . . You who are slaves, give to your human masters the obedience you owe to Christ . . . but in the character of Christ's slaves, who do what is God's will with all their hearts.'

It is our misfortune to live in an age of upheaval. Misguided men and women are demanding enormous social change. The cry from the market place is 'liberty' and the common dream is personal freedom for all men.

How noble it all sounds. The poor man forgets that in his pursuit of liberty he infringes the rights of others. The resultant bitterness leads to strife and chaos in our society.

Let us make one thing clear. The liberty these levellers pursue is a phantom. The stones of this church, given the liberty to move, would topple the building. But man is not a stone and men look for happiness in this life. Wherein lies this happiness? The wise man knows that true happiness lies in the willing submission of man's desires to God's Will. 'Thy Will be Done'.

The stones, the flowers in the field, the trees, the earth and the stars all obey the law of God. They know their place in the universe and in the purpose that God is working out. The law of God calls on man to exercise discipline of mind and subjection of will. Those in authority must use good judgment and be firm in their sense of duty. Those dependent on their superiors must show respect. What respect do we have left in this village, where teachers flout the authority of those over them?

Eland and others freeze.
Enter **Tom, Annie** *and a small group of schoolchildren including* **Emily** *and* **George**. **Tom** *is carrying a rolled-up map.*

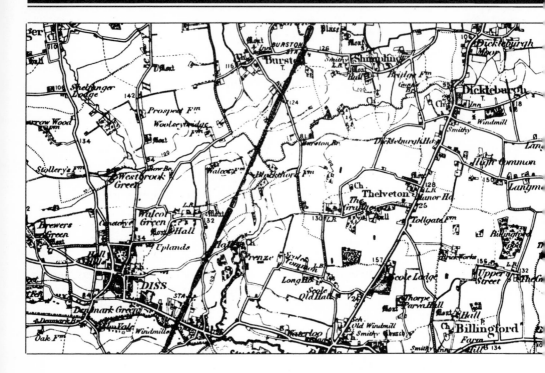

Tom	(*Unrolling the map*) So today we are going to study maps. (*Shows it to the children*) This is a map of Burston. Can anyone point out Burston on the map?
	Emily *points to a spot on the map.*
	Yes, well done.
George	(*Pointing to a spot on the map*) That's Diss, where our parents were fined in the court because of the strike.
Emily	We all marched there, twice.
George	Someone gave us all ice-cream.
Emily	A man took our photograph.
George	We were in the papers.
Emily	First they fined us two shillings and sixpence.

George   The second time it was five bob.

Emily   We marched to Diss and laughed in their faces.

                  They all freeze.
                  Eland *continues his sermon.*

Eland   Teachers who never go to church on Sunday, and preach individual liberty to children in the classroom. Teachers who breed discontent in those who till the land, and lead labourers in defiance of their masters.

                  Enter a ***Glebe Tenant.*** *He walks up to the foot of the pulpit.*

Tenant   Why have you served notice on me? Why are you throwing me off my land? My family has rented it from the church for twenty years.

Eland   I'm not getting into any argument.

Tenant   I've always paid my rent. You're throwing me off my land because we support the Higdons!

Eland   That has nothing to do with it.

Tenant   Then give me a reason.

Eland   It's my business. Listen, lad. If a landlord chooses to give notice, a tenant is obliged to go out. I have a perfect right to give you notice. If you feel aggrieved, you should seek redress through the legal tribunals.

Tenant   I keep my family on forty pounds a year. We feast on bread and lard while Glebe owners munch their biscuits and cream. The law is a luxury I can't afford, and you know it – man of God.

                  The ***Glebe Tenant*** *freezes.*
                  Eland *continues his sermon.*

Eland   Their liberty is licence and reckless disregard for social order. Their liberty permits the rogue to excuse his wrongdoing, the rebel to resort to anarchy, the fool to demand equality and the vicious man to indulge in violence.

St Paul warned us about these false teachers. In his epistle to the
Colossians, he says: 'Take care not to let anyone cheat you with his
philosophizings, or with empty phantasies drawn from human
tradition, from worldly principles; they were never Christ's
teaching'.

Eland freezes.
Enter a **soldier** *in uniform,* **Mr Wilby** *and*
Mr Potter.

Mr Wilby   The Higdons taught those children on the village green for four
weeks.

Mr Potter   The weather finally broke and the strike school had to move into old
blind Ambrose Sandy's place.

Soldier   I know – the carpenter's shop on the edge of Burston Green.

Mr Wilby   They tried to get the inspectors to close the school on the grounds of
safety and hygiene but the inspectors could find no fault in it.

Mr Potter   They couldn't persuade Blind Sandy to evict the school, so they
hounded him out of the village.

Soldier, Mr Wilby *and* **Mr Potter** *freeze.*

Eland   People of Burston, go out and tell your neighbours who have
deserted God's church and God's teaching to follow the dangerous
and subversive example of the false school teachers, that the church
is the foundation stone of society. Shake it, and the wrath of God
will fall on their heads.

Blackout.

· ·

BURSTON SCHOOL STRIKE
A Village in Revolt !

Great Demonstration
OF PROTEST

Against Ejectment Summonses issued

by the Rector against Glebe Tenants.

On Burston Green,
SUNDAY, Nov. 28th,
AT 2.30 P.M.

W. CARTER
(Of London), and N.U.R. Delegates will speak.

**Contingents with BAND and BANNERS will arrive at
12.30 and March through the Village.**

Both the Glebe Tenants have Sons in the Trenches
fighting for their Country, while the Parson is wresting
from their Parents the little bit of Land they occupy.

LUCMOS BROS. PRINTERS, DISS.

Scene 4

*Enter **Mrs Wilby**, **Mrs Potter** and **Mrs Moore**.*

Mrs Wilby   From all around people came to visit us.

Mrs Potter   Trades unions in London held meetings in support of us.

Mrs Moore   The school did well. Soon we had collected enough money to build our own school. We've kept going for three years. No one can stop us now.

*The whole village enter behind the May Queen and her attendants. With them are **Sutton**, **Carter**, **Roberts**, and **Sylvia Pankhurst**. The villagers sing the May Day song: 'It is the First of May'.*

Villagers   Good morning lords and ladies,
It is the first of May,
We hope you'll view our garland,
It is so bright and gay.

CHORUS – Oh it is the first of May,
Oh it is the first of May,
Remember lords and ladies,
It is the first of May.

We gathered them this morning,
All in the early dew,
And now we've brought their beauty
And fragrance all for you.

CHORUS

The cuckoo comes in April,
It sings its song in May,
In June it changes tune,
And July it flies away.

CHORUS

And now you've seen our garland,
We must be on our way,
So remember lords and ladies,
It is the first of May.

CHORUS

Sutton   Friends, on this happy May Day, we have three distinguished
                              speakers who are here to support our cause and celebrate with us
                              the opening of the strike school. First, Mr Carter, who on three
                              occasions has brought thousands of the National Union of
                              Railwaymen here to Burston Green, to boost our efforts and raise
                              our morale. Mr Carter . . .

Carter   Fellow working men and women of Norfolk.
                              With your help, we have raised over a thousand pounds in a few
                              months. The result is the new school, built on the edge of this now
                              famous Burston Green. It will be a free school, a centre of rural
                              democracy and a memorial of the villagers' fight for freedom. There
                              have been delays and difficulties in getting the school built but that
                              is only to be expected in time of a great and tragic war. But now we
                              have built it, the first real workers' elementary school has been
                              provided by the workers themselves. It is a substantial structure,
                              thirty-six feet long and twenty-four feet wide. With the churchyard
                              on one side and the village green in front, a fine playground for the
                              children, it is well situated. The front is faced with Bath stone.
                              Inscribed in the stone are the names of trades unions and societies
                              who have contributed to its cost. Along the top is the inscription:
                              'Burston Strike School'. Long live the strike!

                              Applause as **Carter** *steps down.*

Sutton   And now, from our own Agricultural and Rural Workers Union –
                              Mr Roberts . . .

Roberts   Ladies and gentlemen, a great victory has been won. But Burston
                              has seen a great struggle and there have been examples of bitterness,
                              hate and vengeance in the efforts to suppress the Higdons.
                              Brothers, that struggle cannot cease with the opening of the school.
                              We must fight to reinstate the former tenants of the Glebe lands,
                              who were so unjustly evicted because they supported the cause. One
                              of them was blind; the Parson took his Glebe away because he lent
                              the villagers his shop for the strike school. He took Mr Harry Ling's
                              Glebe away because he would not let his daughter go to a mock
                              inquiry or go himself to tell a lie. He took Mr Garnham's Glebe
                              away because he attended the strike school meetings. Two of these
                              tenants had sons in the Trenches fighting for their country, while
                              the Parson was wresting from their parents the little bit of land they
                              occupied. Our campaign to restore these good people to their
                              rightful holdings is already under way. The struggle continues!

Applause as **Roberts** *steps down.*

Sutton   And now, ladies and gentlemen, I have the honour to present
                        someone known to you all – Miss Sylvia Pankhurst!

Sylvia Pankhurst   The strike school, which we are about to open officially, began on
                        1 April 1914. It has been in existence for more than three years. Yet
                        still the parents, children and teachers, and their supporters in
                        Burston, are solidly united in their protest against injustice and
                        tyranny, and in the fight for freedom. What began as a strike of
                        schoolchildren in support of their teacher, and was spoken of by the
                        Rector, chairman of the school managers, as 'all moonshine' and 'a
                        nine-days wonder' has become a permanent Socialist Educational
                        Cause and Institution, the first trades union school in England. This
                        new building will serve to house what has already become the centre
                        of a new living movement of educational and social activity and it
                        will become the best lasting memorial to the villagers' fight for
                        freedom and justice. Some day, when England is indeed free and
                        the people of her villages are, in fact, as they were once said to be, as
                        joyous and tuneful as a nest of singing birds, the story of the
                        Burston tyranny and revolt will be staged as a popular comedy in
                        London theatres – and whilst the credulous people will marvel at it,
                        the wiseacres will say that it is overdrawn. And today! Whose feet
                        would not dance on such a day as this? May we not hope that at last
                        the longed-for revolution is at hand? For it is not just a local fight.
                        The cause goes to the roots of English life. I, Sylvia Pankhurst,
                        commend the cause of the Burston School Strike to all sections of
                        the Labour Movement.

Applause as **Sylvia Pankhurst** *steps down.*

Sutton   And now, Violet Potter.

Violet   With joy and thankfulness, I declare this school open, to be forever
                        a school of freedom.

Cheers and applause.
The band strikes up with 'England Arise'. The
cast are led by **Tom** *and* **Annie Higdon** *in the*
singing.

All   England arise! The long, long night is over
                        Faint in the east behold the dawn appear
                        Out of your evil dream of toil and sorrow
                        Arise O England, for the day is here
                        From your fields and hills
                        Hark, the answer swells
                        Arise O England, for the day is here.

Activities

What is Education?

Read

It is difficult to imagine quite how different education was at the time of **The Burston School Strike** from what it is like now.

Study the dates below. Next to them are some of the important changes which governments have made between 1870 and 1988. Some of this information will help you understand what happens in the play you have read.

1870
The Government was given power to make local authorities build schools and make children attend school. School boards were set up and directly elected by the ratepayers to run the new schools.

In many country areas it took a long time for this to mean that all children went to school. Many were still under pressure from their parents to work in the fields and earn money for their families. As some of the employers – the landowners and farmers – were also school managers, the pressure on children was sometimes very great.

1873
Fines were introduced for those who did not attend school, but magistrates did not often convict parents.

1880
Children could not leave school until the age of 13 unless they had passed an exam and received a labour certificate. This meant that many clever children left school earlier rather than staying on to learn more.

1874
The minimum age at which children could be in full-time employment was raised from 13 to 14.

1891
The idea that education was free was introduced. (Before this time some state schools had charged fees.)

1902
School boards were abolished and local education authorities were set up.

1918
The official age for leaving school for *all* children was raised to 14.

1944

The official leaving age was raised to 15. Free school milk was introduced. Primary and secondary schools were set up. Many other important changes were made to improve the quality of education in schools.

1973

The official age for leaving school was raised to 16.

1988

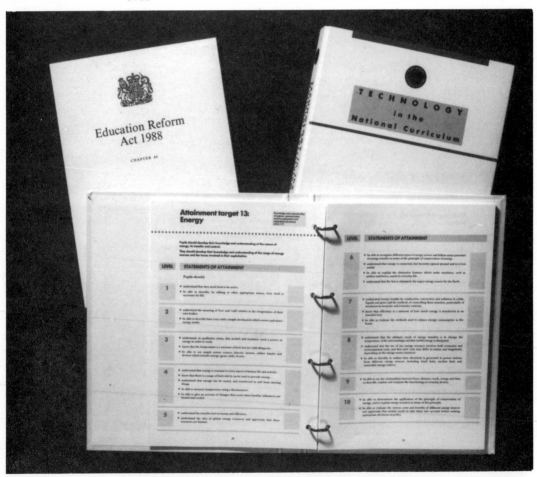

The National Curriculum was introduced. For the first time schools were told which subjects they had to teach: English, maths, science, technology, art, music, geography, history, religious and physical education and a modern foreign language.

Talk

1 How old do the children in this play seem to be? What makes you think this?

2 Do they seem to be the same age as each other?

3 Read Act 1, Scenes 1 and 2 again. How is the school at Burston unlike your own or any others that you have been to in the past? Make a list of all the ways in which it is different. Which of the differences do you think are the most important?

4 Do you get the impression that the children enjoy going to school and being taught by Annie Higdon? Explain your answer. Do you think you would have liked being taught by the Higdons?

5 The first 'subject' or activity that Annie Higdon makes the children take part in is music when they sing 'Early One Morning'. What other activities make up their school work? In pairs, go through the play and decide what you think they are being taught.

What is School For?

Talk

1   What do you think you are taught at school? Make two lists. In the first write down everything that is taught at school. In the second, put down everything that you can think of that isn't. You might want to look again at page 62.

Taught in school	Not taught
Music	Self defence
English	How to be happy
Word-processing	

2   Why do you think you are taught the 'subjects' you have included in the left hand column?

3   Underline the 'subjects' that you think are more important than the others and explain why you have done this.

4   Are there any other things that you learn at school which are not 'subjects'? If so, what are they?

5   What do you think are the three most important issues facing young people when they leave school? Are you taught about these in your school?

6   Do you think that most learning happens inside or outside the classroom? Why?

7   Using the information about the play on pages 60 to 62 and your own knowledge and experience, decide what you think are the three or four most exciting changes that have happened in education since the early 1900s.

Think

In small groups, plan your own school timetable for someone of your own age. Before you do this, think about this extract from *Alice in Wonderland* by Lewis Carroll.

> 'Cheshire-Puss,' she began, rather timidly . . . 'would you tell me, please, which way I ought to go from here?'
> 'That depends a good deal on where you want to get to,' said the cat.
> 'I don't much care where . . .' said Alice.
> 'Then it doesn't matter which way you go,' said the cat.

Decide:
- where you want to get to
- what kind of school you will be part of
- what kind of 'lessons' it might have
- what kind of subjects it might have
- if it will be inside or, like the strike school in the play, outside, or both.

Copy and complete the timetable below.

Name .... School			
Monday			
Tuesday			
Wednesday			
Thursday			
Friday			

Times of day →   Lunch

Schools in the Future

Read

What do you think schools will be like a hundred years from now? To get you thinking, read what one writer has predicted might happen. The extract is from *Examination Day* by Henry Slesar.

Examination Day

At five minutes to eleven, they called the name of Jordan.

'Good luck, son,' his father said, without looking at him. 'I'll call for you when the test is over.'

Dickie walked to the door and turned the handle. The room inside was dim, and he could hardly make out the features of the grey-tunicked attendant who greeted him.

'Sit down,' the man said softly. He indicated a high stool beside his desk. 'Your name's Richard Jordan?'

'Yes, sir.'

'Your classification is 600-115. Drink this, Richard.'

He lifted a plastic cup from the desk and handed it to the boy. The liquid inside it had the consistency of buttermilk and tasted vaguely of peppermint. Dickie downed it, and handed the man the empty cup.

He sat in silence, feeling drowsy, while the man wrote busily on a sheet of paper. Then the attendant looked at his watch, and rose to stand only inches from Dickie's face. He unclipped a penlike object from the pocket of his tunic and flashed a tiny light into the boy's eyes.

'All right,' he said. 'Come with me, Richard.'

He led Dickie to the end of the room, where a single wooden armchair faced a multi-dialled computing machine. There was a microphone on the left arm of the chair, and when the boy sat down, he found its pinpoint head conveniently at his mouth.

'Now just relax, Richard. You'll be asked some questions, and you think them over carefully. Then give your answers into the microphone. The machine will take care of the rest.'

'Yes, sir.'

'I'll leave you alone now. Whenever you want to start, just say "ready" into the microphone.'

'Yes, sir.'

The man squeezed his shoulder, and left.

Dickie said, 'Ready.'

• •

Lights appeared on the machine, and a mechanism whirred. A voice said:

'Complete this sequence. One, four, seven, ten . . .'

★

Mr and Mrs Jordan were in the living room, not speaking, not even speculating.

It was almost four o'clock when the telephone rang. The woman tried to reach it first, but her husband was quicker.

'Mr Jordan?'

The voice was clipped; a brisk, official voice.

'Yes, speaking.'

'This is the Government Educational Service. Your son, Richard M. Jordan, Classification 600–115, has completed the Government examination. We regret to inform you that his intelligence quotient has exceeded the Government regulation, according to Rule 84, Section 5, of the New Code.'

Across the room, the woman cried out, knowing nothing except the emotion she read on her husband's face.

'You may specify by telephone,' the voice droned on, 'whether you wish his body interred by the Government or would you prefer a private burial place? The fee for Government burial is ten dollars.'

Henry Slesar

• •

Talk

1   What kind of world do you think is being decribed here?

2   How far in the future do you think it is set?

3   What do you think happens to Richard Jordan? Why?

• •

Write

Decide what you think might change in education in the future. Write your own story about what schools might be like one hundred years from now.

Who Does What in the Play?

Talk

Here are some of the kinds of people who played a part in **The Burston School Strike**.

- School managers
- Teachers
- Norfolk County Council
- Parents
- The Government

Decide which kinds of people each of the characters in the play are. You may need to refer back to the character list on pages 8 and 9.

Write   **1**   How are these different kinds of people linked together in the play?

          2   Draw a diagram to show the way you think they are connected. It might look
                   like one of these:

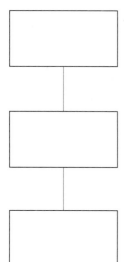
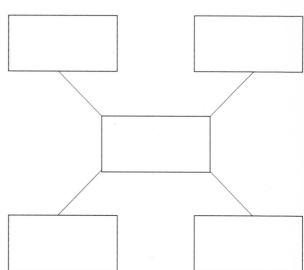

                   Or you might choose another way of describing it.

          3   Do the same thing for your own school now, using the list below and any other
                   kinds of people you can think of.

          ● Nurse   ● Parents
          ● Teachers   ● Local Education Authority
          ● Pupils   ● Deputy Head
          ● Caretakers   ● Welfare staff
          ● Canteen staff   ● Secretary
          ● School governors   ● The Government
          ● Headteacher

What Makes a Good Teacher?

Read

About forty years before the Burston School Strike these were the things that people in one area of America thought made a good teacher.

---

*R*ules for teachers in America, 1879

1 Teachers each day will fill lamps, clean chimneys, before beginning work.

2 Each teacher will bring a bucket of water and a scuttle of coal for the day's session.

3 Make your pens carefully; you may whittle nibs to the individual tastes of the children.

4 Men teachers may take one evening a week for courting purposes or two evenings to attend church regularly.

5 After 10 hours in school you may spend the remaining time reading the bible or other good books.

6 Women teachers who marry or engage in other unseemly conduct will be dismissed.

7 Every teacher should lay aside from each pay a good sum for his benefit during his declining years so that he will not become a burden on society.

8 Any teacher who smokes, uses liquor in any form, frequents pool or public halls, or gets shaved in a barber's shop, will give good reason to suspect his worth, intention, integrity and honesty.

Talk

1 Which of these rules surprised you the most and why?

2 Which of these rules do you think the Reverend Eland would have approved of?

Write

What 'rules' do you think the school managers of Burston School would have written down? Make a list of what they might have been.

Talk

1 What qualities do you think make an ideal teacher? Do you think that Annie and Tom Higdon have some of these? If so, which? Is it to do with knowing a lot, being able to keep order, being amusing, or is to do with other qualities?

2 In pairs make a checklist of the qualities you think are necessary, making it clear which you think are the most important.

. . . .

Who is in the Right?

Talk

There are many different opinions expressed in **The Burston School Strike**, as there were in real life when the events it shows actually happened. Who do you think was right?

To help you decide, study these quotations. For each one, decide:
- who said it
- where it comes in the play
- why it is said
- how much you agree with what is being said.

This is a farming community, Mr Higdon. The children are expected to help their elders at need.

It's a lot of lies! Mrs Higdon never ill-treated those girls!

...it is to the interest of the elementary education in this village that the head teacher should seek other employment with as little delay as possible.

The children need education as well as learning love of the land. You school managers are undermining our efforts to teach them...

We know they're good teachers and we don't want them replaced with Parson's people and parish busybodies.

The lad'll learn more at the plough than anything you and your lady wife can teach him!

It is our misfortune to live in an age of upheaval. Misguided men and women are demanding enormous social change.

The Higdons care about our children – you can tell that.

Christianity goes beyond one church, Mr Eland. It is around us indoors and out, and we benefit daily from its influence.

He's a school teacher – he should keep his meddling fingers off the farms.

The History Behind the Play

Annie   We walked out of Wood Dalling, Tom – we'll walk into Burston.

Mrs Ling   There's a photograph of our husbands on the front page.

Read

The Burston School Strike is based on real events. When it was being written, Roy Nevitt visited Burston and talked to Violet Potter and others who had actually been involved in this piece of our history.

As well as the people he was able to see, there were many other kinds of documents to help him – the school logbook, letters, photographs, newspaper articles, and accounts, for example.

Many of these are referred to in the play.

Read through these pages carefully. They contain a brief account of what happened, followed by a longer version which includes various documents. You can draw your own conclusions from these.

A Brief Account

The Higdons' story really begins at Wood Dalling, nine years before this play starts. Here they were headmistress and assistant teacher. As a result of the stand they made over the illegal employment of school children, and disagreements they had with the school managers, they were transferred to Burston.

Norfolk Education Committee

EDUCATION DEPARTMENT,

SHIREHALL,

NORWICH.

2nd August 1910.

<u>WOOD DALLING SCHOOL.</u>

Dear Madam,

   The Sub-Committee's Report on their recent enquiry into the complaint made against you, was considered by the Committee on Saturday last.
   The Sub-Committee reported that they found the complaint fully proved. After giving the matter full consideration, the Committee decided to allow you to send in your resignation, this being the course of action which would be least prejudicial to you. I shall be glad therefore to receive your resignation in accordance with the above resolution.

                    Yours faithfully,

• •

On January 31st 1911, Tom and Annie Higdon arrived in Burston, a small Norfolk village. They had walked from Diss, five miles away, because the train had failed to stop at the local station.

One of the first people they met was Harry Ellis, the village postman. He thought they said their name was 'Kingdom' not 'Higdon' and it was at school the next day that the mistake was corrected. The local school had had a number of different teachers in recent years and the children were used to new arrivals.

For the next two years there was little to disturb the calm of the village. Tom and Annie Higdon went about the job of teaching the farming children with enthusiasm. They enjoyed nature rambles in the woods, cooking in the schoolroom and a sort of learning that was more exciting than that going on in many of the classrooms of the day.

During this time the clerk to the managers of the school was to write of Tom Higdon:

'. . . he is under my frequent observation and I have found his conduct and bearing exemplary in every respect. He is zealous and industrious, punctual and energetic. He is also tactful and held in esteem by parents. He holds his present appointment with his wife; the discipline and organization of the school is all that can be desired.'

Burston School Logbook

1911

February 1st Annie R. Higdon took charge. Thomas G. Higdon commenced duties.

February 17th. The smoking of the stove which is in a very bad state, resembles a "pea-soup" fog and is so dirty and uncomfortable and continual that the lighting of the stove has been discontinued, –the cold being less trying than the daily smoke...

1911

November 28th. Children warned against the danger of standing in the road before approaching motors.

December 7th. Schoolroom so dark at 9 a.m. that mistress could not see the children's eyes as they stood singing their morning hymn.

December 15th. At 2.15 p.m. it was again too dark for the children to see to do their work. The lamp glasses recently ordered are not yet come.

1912

September 17th. Re-opened an extra week and one day being required for alterations. The new window adds a beautiful light to the room.

Inspected on 11th October 1912

General:—

The present Mistress has had charge of the School a little over a year and a half, and its condition is now very promising. A good tone prevails; the scholars take pride in their work, and the work done in some of the subjects of instruction is very creditable. Mental Arithmetic is well above the average and the written Arithmetic of the First Class is generally praiseworthy. The Singing and much of the Drawing are good and needlework is being taught on sensible lines.

On the whole, the Infants and the First Class children are making more progress than the scholars in the middle section of the school.

A year and a half later, Mrs Higdon was to receive the following letter from the Secretary of the Norfolk Education Committee:

Dear Madam,

In a communication received from the Managers on the 13th of November, the committee were asked if they 'will kindly remove Mrs. Higdon to a sphere more genial.'

I may remind you that this is the second place in which you have come into conflict with the managers.

The letter went on to criticize Mrs Higdon for lighting fires when the school managers had said she should not.

Read

To begin to understand how all this led to so much change, look carefully at these pages. Remember there is no one interpretation of history. You will need to make up your own mind as to what went wrong and why!

March 1913

Noah Sandy asked Tom Higdon to help him fight the parish council elections. He wanted the workers in the area to be represented instead of a majority of landowners and farmers. In a packed schoolroom their plans succeeded. Only one farmer was elected, Tom Higdon was top of the poll and the Rector was bottom with only nine votes.

Church attendance

Mrs Higdon was a 'chapelgoer'. She only occasionally went to services at the local Church of England where the Rector, Eland, officiated.

School closure

Following an epidemic of whooping cough, Mrs Higdon decided to close the school for a week. She consulted the vice-chairman of the managers who agreed. The chairman, Eland, was on holiday in Switzerland. On his return he informed Mrs Higdon that he and the managers' committee took a very serious view of her having closed the school without permission.

The school fire

The Reverend Eland objected to the fire being lit without permission. Mrs Higdon said this was done on wet mornings to dry children's clothes because the third radiator of the heating apparatus did not sufficiently warm the room.

December 10th 1913: The Barnardo children

Two children from a Dr Barnardo home were living with a foster mother, Mrs Philpot. They were involved in an incident in the playground and Mrs Philpot complained. The facts of the case were disputed by Mr and Mrs Higdon who thought the girls were lying. The managers considered the case and there were complaints that the girls had been caned in school for deceit. This was denied by the Higdons and evidence was produced to show that the boy who was supposed to have provoked the incident in the playground had been absent on the day in question. Witnesses to the later inquiry were not given the chance to say how Mrs Philpot had frequently beaten the girls.

February 23rd and 27th 1914

The school managers had asked the Norfolk Education Committee to sack the teachers. A sub-committee found:

> 'that the head teacher had been discourteous to the managers.'

The sub-committee, after most carefully reviewing the whole of the evidence, advised:

> 'that it is to the interest of elementary education in the village that the head teacher should seek other employment with as little delay as possible. That

no punishment book having been kept in this school by the head teacher prior to this occurrence, she be directed faithfully to keep such a book'.

On March 31st 1914, the Higdons were dismissed.

Mr Ikin, from the Education Authority, called to give Tom and Annie Higdon pay in lieu of notice on April 1st 1914. He also wanted to know when they would be moving out. The teachers were upset. They had little inclination to move. They felt their dismissal unjust and, in any case, why could they not work out their three months' notice?

The day before, many of the parents had met by lamplight on the village green. Led by George Durbidge, many decided to keep their children from the school in the hope that the teachers would be re-employed. Many believed Tom Higdon had been 'victimized' for his political work.

Violet Potter, one of the senior girls, had written down the names of all the children willing to go on strike. They chalked on the blackboard: 'We are going on strike tomorrow'. The same sign was chalked on other parts of the village.

Burston School Logbook

1913
March 10th. The schoolroom shows several signs of recent public entertainment held during past Thurs and Friday evenings. The top of the mistress' desk was used as a floor for hobnailed boots and is very badly scratched and roughed. The children's desks were also stood upon and covered with mud and scratches from the heavy boots of village youth...

1914

April 1st. I, Edna Howard, take charge of this school today as temporary Head Teacher with Miss G. Thurlow from Trowse School as Assistant. Only 6 senior children have been present morning and afternoon and 19 infants in the morning and 7 in the afternoon. The others are on strike.

April 23rd. Eighteen parents were summoned before Diss Bench yesterday for keeping their children from school and were each fined 2/6.

Sept 14th. School reopened with 9 children. 8 as before the holiday, and Amy Norman from the "Strike" school.

'Our School Strike' by Emily Wilby

We came on strike on April 1st, 1914. We came on strike because our Governess and Master were dismissed from the Council School unjustly. The Parson got two Barnardo children to say that our Governess had caned them and slapped their faces, but we all know she did not. Then our Governess lit a fire one wet morning to dry some of our clothes without asking the Parson. So the head ones said that our Governess and Master had better be got rid of. They had their pay sent and two days' notice to leave the school. Governess did not know we were going on strike. She bought us all some Easter eggs and oranges the last day we were at the Council School.

Violet Potter brought a paper to school with all our names on it, and all who were going on strike had to put a cross against their name. Out of seventy-two children sixty-six came out on strike.

The first morning our mothers sent the infants because they thought they did not matter, but in the afternoon they too stopped away and only six answered the bell.

The next morning the sixty-six children lined up on the Crossways. We all had cards around our necks and paper trimmings. We marched past the Council school and round the 'Candlestick'. When we got to the foster-mother's house she came out with a dustpan and brush to 'tin' us, but when she saw our mothers she ran in. She put a card in her window with 'Victory' on it, but she has not got it yet. Some of our parents gave us cake and drink and many other things. When we got to the Crown Common we had a rest. Mrs Boulton, the lady at the Post Office, gave us some lemonade and sweets and nuts. She also gave us a large banner and several flags. At twelve o'clock we went home for dinner. At one we marched again. When we got up to one of the foster-mother's friends (who is a foster-mother too) she jumped up from behind a hedge and began to 'tin' us. When we hooted her she said she would summons us, but it has not happened yet.

Emily Wilby was one of the strike school pupils. She wrote this in 1915.

The strike

The children formed up in the village and with banners saying 'Justice' and 'We want our teachers back' they marched past Mr Ikin singing at the top of their voices. Even the presence of policemen failed to stop them.

The weather was fine. Tom and Annie Higdon gave lessons on the green and the children stayed on strike. The attendance officer, Mr Starr, served summonses on twenty of the parents and when the case was first heard a great many people joined in the march to the magistrate's court at Diss.

Despite fines the parents kept their children away from the council school. A second series of summonses were served and fines of five shillings imposed. But after this the court cases were dropped. The carpenter had given his shop for the school. The children were being taught by qualified teachers who on a number of occasions in the past had been commended by His Majesty's Inspectors of Schools.

By now the case was receiving national publicity. The Agricultural Labourers' Union paid for the legal representation of parents at the second magistrates hearing. The Union of Railwaymen joined in a huge demonstration on November 10th 1915 when nine London branches were represented with their banners.

Collections were held all over the country and eventually one thousand, six hundred and sixty-two pounds nine shillings and a ha'penny was raised to build a new school to house the strike children. Donations included:

Burston School Strike	BALANCE SHEET		
INCOME			
	£	s.	d.
Miners	401	17	0
Railwaymen's Branches	288	11	0
Other Societies	211	12	8
Trades and Labour Councils	183	12	4
Co-operative Societies	221	15	0
Private Subscriptions	171	9	2
L.L.P. Branches	52	7	11
Typographical Branches	25	11	6
Enginemen and Firemen's Branches	13	3	6
Boot and Shoe Branches	11	17	6
Carpenters' and Joiners' Branches	10	0	0
London Optical Glass Society	10	0	0
Gas Workers	9	3	5

Trades unions and labour organizations throughout the country saw in the Burston School Strike a good example of the way workers needed to unite to secure fair and just working conditions.

Controversy in the village was to rage for many years. The vicar evicted some tenants from 'glebe land' he controlled and it was thought the reason was their support of the strike. The church was boycotted by a number of families and the strike school prospered for many years attracting children from all over the country.

The school survived up until the Second World War, although at the end there was only a handful of children. Tom Higdon died in 1939 and Annie in 1946. The school is now a village hall and social centre.

Different Points of View

Talk

1   How closely do you think Roy Nevitt has followed the events described in these accounts?

2   Make a list of anything
    • described in these pages which is not included in the play
    • described here which is treated differently in the play.

What Happened When?

Write

Copy and complete this timeline of events in the play using the background information to help you.

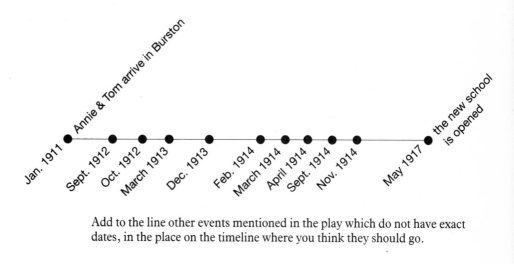

Add to the line other events mentioned in the play which do not have exact dates, in the place on the timeline where you think they should go.

The Children

Write

What do you think it must have been like to have lessons on Burston Green?

Imagine that you were one of the children in the play and that you kept a diary between 1912 and 1915.

Choose three special days from this time to write up in your diary. For example, you might choose the day the Higdons arrived, the day you went on strike (if you did) and a day on the village green. Or you could choose different days and describe some of the events you have been reading about in the play.

Talk

1   If you had been at Burston, would you have wanted to be at school or helping your family in the fields?

2   Do you do paid work now? How many of your friends have part-time jobs?

3   Look at this survey conducted by the Low Pay Unit recently. It shows the jobs that young people currently do, some of them illegally.

Delivering newspapers	Sewing or making things to sell
Milk round or other deliveries	Typing, filing or book-keeping
Newsagency or tobacconists	Pub or off-licence
Grocery, bakery or other food shop	Hotel, restaurant, cafe or take-away
Clothing or department store	Street market or fairground
Shoe shop	Modelling, acting or dancing
Other shop or store	professionally
Hairdressers	Stable, kennel or riding school
Launderette or dry-cleaners	Other work with animals outside
Cleaning offices, hotels or homes	the home
Furniture removals or furniture	Farming or gardening
making	Car washing
Constructing, decorating or	Voluntary work
repairing buildings	Bingo ticket selling, snooker hall
Garage or petrol station	Selling food (ice-cream van etc)

Conduct a survey to find out how many of these jobs are done by people in your class.

4   What are the main reasons why children work? Should adults be doing this work?

5   Find out which jobs people of your own age are legally allowed to do.

NB *The Children and Young Persons Act 1933* states that no child may be employed until he or she has reached the age of thirteen, and then only on a limited basis until compulsory school-leaving age. *The Employment of Women, Young Persons and Children Act 1920* prohibits the employment of children in an 'industrial undertaking' eg: mines, quarries, industrial manufacturing, construction, etc.

The Teachers

Role Play

How do you think you would have felt if you had been Tom or Annie Higdon? In pairs, choose a moment in the play when something important has just happened. It could be the parish elections, the strike or any moment of your choice.

Imagine you are Tom and Annie. Decide where you are and what you are thinking and feeling. Have a conversation together.

Write

Look back at the extracts from the Burston School logbook on pages 74 and 75.

Choose a series of days from the play which are not covered in these extracts. Write a number of entries as you think Annie Higdon would have done.

· ·

The Wider Community

Talk   What did other people think of the school and its strike? Who were the main
                      people against it? Who supported it?

                      What would you have done?

· ·

Read   Study these two national newspaper articles which appeared at the time.

SCHOLARS' STRIKE
BANNERS INSCRIBED 'WE WANT OUR TEACHERS BACK'

The children of the Council School of Burston and Shimpling, Norfolk, have gone on strike as a protest against the dismissal of the Headmistress, Mrs. Higdon, and her husband, who was also on the school staff.

Yesterday only seven scholars met the two imported teachers. The other children paraded the district carrying a banner inscribed 'We Want Our Teachers Back.'

The dispute originated in complaints made by the school managers, of whom the Rev. C.T. Eland, Rector of Burston, is Chairman, that Mrs. Higdon had ill-treated children from Dr. Barnardo's Homes. The mistress and her husband totally denied the allegation, and asked for an inquiry. The County Committee investigated the matter with the result that Mr. and Mrs. Higdon were called upon to resign.

The sympathy of the inhabitants is strongly with the deposed teachers, and the opinion is freely expressed that political motives underlie the matter, Mr. Higdon's views on politics being opposed to those of the rector and the majority of the managers.

Public meetings have protested by large majorities against the dismissals and resolutions have been passed declaring that Mr. and Mrs. Higdon have been unfairly treated.

Children strike because of teachers' dismissal

In sympathy with their dismissed teachers, Mr. and Mrs. T.G. Higdon, 62 out of 70 children attending the village school at Burston, Norfolk, have gone 'on strike'. They are supported in most instances by their parents, several of whom have been fined by the Diss magistrates.

The parents demand an official explanation from the Norfolk Education Committee of the dismissal of Mrs. Higdon, the head mistress, and her husband, the assistant master, and they insist also on a public enquiry to clear up a mystery surrounding the causes of the committee's action.

Both Mr. and Mrs. Higdon are supporters of the Agricultural Workers' Union, and Mr. Higdon is an official. 'I am a labourers' man – that's the top and the bottom of it,' he declared yesterday.

Both the teachers were dismissed, with salary in lieu of notice, after a private enquiry.

. . . .

Talk   What do you think the writers of these two articles thought about the strike? Why?

. . . .

Write   Choose one of these types of people – a school manager, a sympathetic parent, the village carpenter, the Reverend Eland. Imagine you have been asked to write a newspaper article for one of these two national newspapers in which you express your opinions about the strike. Use the play and the information you have been studying to help you do this.

. . . .

Standing Up For Your Rights

Talk   What would you be prepared to take action for?

1   In groups, make a list of all the things you feel strongly about and might take some kind of action for.

2   What do you think are the most effective ways for young people to make a protest? Do you know of any which have been as successful as the strike in this play?

3   Is there anything that you can imagine happening in your school that you would feel strongly enough about to consider striking or making some kind of protest for?

Songs in the Play

Music

Here is the music for two of the songs in this play. In the original performance they were accompanied by an accordion. You might like to try them out with a guitar, piano or any other musical instrument of your choice.

England, Arise!

Words and music by Edward Carpenter

Eng - land, a - rise! the long, long night is o - ver,

Faint in the east be - hold the dawn ap - pear; Out of your

e - vil dream of toil and sor - row A - rise, O Eng - land, for the

day is here; From your fields and hills, Hark! the an - swer

swells A - rise, O Eng - land, for the day is here!

The Red Flag

Moderato

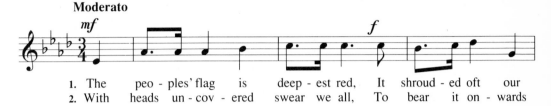

1. The peo - ples' flag is deep - est red, It shroud - ed oft our
2. With heads un - cov - ered swear we all, To bear it on - wards

mar - tyred dead, And ere their limbs grew stiff and cold, Their
till we fall, Come dun - geons dark and gall - ows grim, This

hearts' blood stained its ev - ery fold. *So raise the scar - let*
song shall be our batt - le hymn.

stan - dard high, Be - neath its shade we'll live or die, Though

cow - ards flinch and trai - tors sneer, We'll keep the red flag fly - ing here.

What the Playwright Says: A Guide to Documentary Drama

Read

In these pages, Roy Nevitt describes the various stages that you need to go through to produce a play like **The Burston School Strike**.

The idea

It could be anything – a story somebody tells you, something that happened locally, some strange words on a tombstone in a local churchyard, a bundle of letters somebody kept...

Collection of original materials

You will need to collect as many authentic documents, eyewitness accounts, photographs, reports, minutes of meetings, tape-recorded memories or whatever, relating to your chosen event in history.

The shape of the story

When you have collected documents and other information, you need to work out how a story-line is going to develop. You must decide where to begin and where to end. It felt good to end the first act with a climax: the Higdons have been sacked and the idea of the strike has been announced by Violet Potter. As I wanted to end on a note of celebration, I chose to end the play when the new school was opened. The whole play is a gradual build-up of excitement and involvement.

Characters

At this stage it is important to choose a number of characters on which the action will focus. Obviously the more people you can find out about, the more people can be involved.

Dialogue

A play, of course, works through dialogue – what people say. Sometimes you may be able to find a record of what was actually said and include it. Ideally you would not have to invent any dialogue but in practice, you may have to. In the case of Burston, the real people whose story was told in the play came to see it and said, yes, that was how it was!

Putting the scenes in order

As your material grows, you have to put it into some kind of order. Here you need to try and balance your scenes with each other, a serious one and then a lighter one, changes in mood and intensity. I like to fill the stage with crowds and colour from time to time and to include songs to break up the action.

Time and place

It is essential to have a very clear idea of time and place. When you have chosen the characters and decided what happens between them, you have to know where the action is taking place. The railway station? The turnip field? The schoolroom? What is the weather like? Is it morning? Afternoon? Without these things the actors will be working in a vacuum.

Involving people: a draft script

Several minds are better than one, and when you have got your draft script it is time to start trying scenes out with the actors. This helps you make any necessary changes.

Rehearsing

At this point you will want to have a large group of people involved, ready to do all the jobs which are needed to put on a play.

Performing your play

Eventually you have to decide on a final version and this is the one that you will use for your production. A documentary play is a marvellous way of celebrating history, and a local story can be just as important and exciting as any story that was ever told of kings or queens.

. . . .

Writing a Documentary Drama

Write

Make up your own documentary play or a scene for it based on something that has actually happened.

Start by finding out if your own school has an interesting history. See if there is a school logbook. If it was built fairly recently, then find out if there was another school in the area at the time of the Burston Strike.

Or there might be something that you have heard as a story, possibly to do with your own family.

Or you might know about some interesting piece of local history to investigate.

Or perhaps you would like to choose something from a local newspaper from the past or the present. It doesn't have to be 'old' history!

In groups, try to produce your own mini-documentary drama. Read what Roy Nevitt says on pages 88 to 89 and use as much of it as you can to help you.

Drama Ideas

Improvise 1 **Farmwork or school work?**

Try this out in pairs.
One of you is a farmer employing men, women and children on the farm. You have a field in which you need to sow barley within two days, but first it must be cleared of stones by children.

The other is a child who really likes school. The farmer wants you to work on his field stone-picking. You are afraid of the farmer but your parents need the money and could be evicted from their cottage if you upset the farmer.

Improvise a conversation in which the farmer stops you on your way to school.

Then try this.
One of you is a farmer and the other is a teacher.

The farmer wants to take a child out of school to work in the field. The teacher wants to see the law upheld. Start with the farmer coming into the school to see the teacher.

2 **The train**

Split into groups of four. One pair of each group is A, the other B.

For pair A:
Look at this extract from a well-known hymn.

'The rich man in his castle,   'All things bright and beautiful,
The poor man at his gate,   All creatures great and small,
He made them high and lowly,   All things wise and wonderful,
And ordered their estate.'   The Lord God made them all.'

This represents the Reverend Eland's view of the world.

For pair B:
Look at this extract from *Acts of Apostles Ch4, V 32–35*

'The group of believers was one in mind and heart. No one said that any of his belongings was his own, but they all shared with one another everything they had . . . There was no one in the group who was in need. Those who owned fields or houses would sell them . . . and the money was distributed to each one according to his need.'

This represents Annie Higdon's view of the world.

Talk about what you think your passage means. Imagine you really believe it.

You are in a train compartment, the As are sitting opposite the B's. After 30 seconds of silence one of you drops a bit of paper with your passage written on it. The opposing pair picks it up. Start a conversation perhaps by asking the question, 'Do you really believe this?' or by expressing your own opinions.

See if you can develop a scene out of this. After a while you could join up with another pair.

3 An alternative scene

In groups, make up a scene for the play which does not appear in Roy Nevitt's version, but which you think could have happened.

For example, you could produce an extra scene in the schoolroom when something unusual happens and the Reverend Eland or a school manager comes in.

Act   ### 4 Acting out the play

Choose a scene from the play:
- decide who will play the parts
- decide who will be the director
- decide what props you need
- rehearse it and present it to your class.

This play could not have been written without the extraordinary contribution of Bert Edwards. Indeed, the whole story of what happened in Burston had almost vanished, when Bert, a schoolteacher in Hitchin, came across a reference to the Strike in a history of the Farmworkers' Union, *Sharpen the Sickle* by Reg Groves. Realizing that some of the children must still be living, though getting old now, he turned detective and started tracking them down. He found about twenty of them, many still living in Norfolk. They were keen to tell their story and after two years of research, including the collection of photographs, press-cuttings, letters, recorded interviews and other documents, his book *The Burston School Strike* was published by Lawrence and Wishart, in 1974.

Roy Nevitt was inspired by the story and contacted the author, who lent him all his unpublished source materials and introduced him to Violet Potter and the other strikers who were still alive. Bert arranged for the Burston villagers to come to see the play, which was first performed by The Stantonbury Campus Drama Group in 1975.

Since Bert Edwards' rediscovery of the school strike, the story has attracted widespread attention. Much of the research and some of the ideas used in the follow-up material are based on work produced by The Living Archive Project at Stantonbury Campus, by Norfolk TIE and an Open University Course booklet which focused on the cross-curricular work on the story being developed at Stantonbury Campus.

We would also like to thank David Farmer and the members of TieBreak Touring Theatre Group, Norwich, whose teacher's pack, *The Burston Story*, provided ideas for a further work on the play.

Acknowledgements

Quotations from the Bible used in the play are from
the Ronald Knox translation of the *Holy Bible*,
published by Burns & Oates Ltd., reproduced by
permission of the publishers; quotations in the activity
section are from the *Good News Bible*, published by
the Bible Society/Harper Collins, reproduced by
permission of the publishers; 'Examination Day' by
Henry Slesar, © Henry Slesar 1958, from *The
Playboy Book of Science Fiction and Fantasy*, is
reproduced by permission of the author; 'Our School
Strike' by Emily Wilby, from *The Burston School
Strike* by Bert Edwards, is reproduced by permission
of the publishers, Lawrence & Wishart Ltd.; 'The
Union Song' is an adapted version of a traditional song
which is recorded in *The Painful Plough* (Cambridge
University Press), selected and edited by Roy Palmer;
the music of 'England Arise' by Edward Carpenter, is
an adaptation, © 1992 Oxford University Press, of the
arrangement published in 1906 by J. Curwen & Sons
Ltd.

The illustrations are by Judy Stevens.

The handwriting is by Elitta Fell.

The publishers would like to thank the following for
permission to reproduce photographs:

Michael Dudley p.62; Sally and Richard Greenhill
p.63; The Illustrated London News p.60; The Living
Archive Project p.9, p.27, p.57, p.61, p.72; Norfolk
County Council Library and Information Service
p.50; Roy Nevitt p.2, p.53.